Mental Maths

Key Stage 2
For ages 7-9

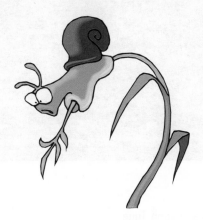

Practise & Learn

Published by CGP

Editors:
Jane Ellingham
Chris Lindle
Rebecca Tate

Updated by Rob Harrison and Ceara Hayden

With thanks to David Ryan for the proofreading.

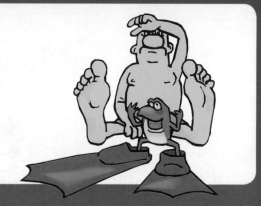

ISBN: 978 1 84762 963 0

Printed by Elanders Ltd, Newcastle upon Tyne
Clipart from Corel®

Contents

Adding & Subtracting 1s, 10s, 100s ...

You can add and subtract by counting on in ones, tens, hundreds or thousands. Here are some examples:

$$628 + 3 = 628 \overset{+1}{\to} 629 \overset{+1}{\to} 630 \overset{+1}{\to} \boxed{631}$$

$$110 - 20 = 110 \overset{-10}{\to} 100 \overset{-10}{\to} \boxed{90}$$

$$120 + 200 = 120 \overset{+100}{\to} 220 \overset{+100}{\to} \boxed{320}$$

$$3700 - 1000 = 3700 \overset{-1000}{\to} \boxed{2700}$$

Complete the additions and write the answers in the boxes.

100 + 5 = **105**		520 + 9 = ☐
231 + 60 = ☐		378 + 20 = ☐
149 + 300 = ☐		645 + 200 = ☐

Complete the subtractions and write the answers in the boxes.

288 − 6 = **282**		323 − 3 = ☐
969 − 20 = ☐		561 − 40 = ☐
540 − 500 = ☐		765 − 600 = ☐

Write the answers to the calculations in the circles.

20 → +40 → 60 → −30 → ◯ → +10 → ◯ → +20 → ◯

◯ ← −30 ◯ ← −20 ◯ ← +40 ◯ ↙ −30

Write the missing numbers in the boxes.

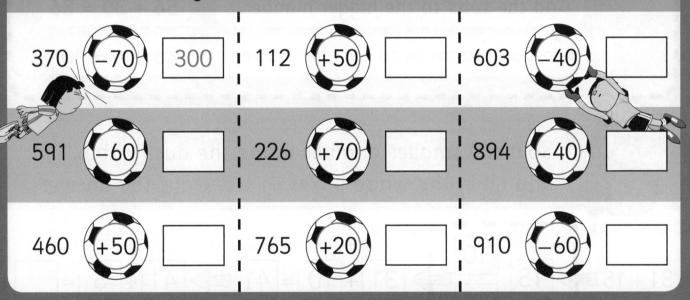

370 −70 → 300	112 +50 → ☐	603 −40 → ☐
591 −60 → ☐	226 +70 → ☐	894 −40 → ☐
460 +50 → ☐	765 +20 → ☐	910 −60 → ☐

Fill in the empty boxes to complete each calculation.

230	+100 →	330	550	−300 →	☐	403	+200 →	☐
820	−400 →	☐	109	+600 →	☐	380	−100 →	☐

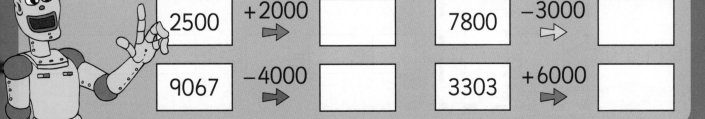

2500	+2000 →	☐	7800	−3000 →	☐
9067	−4000 →	☐	3303	+6000 →	☐

Addition

Adding numbers in your head can be tricky.
One way to make it easier is to split them up.
Here's an example:

34 + 56 = ?

Keep the bigger number whole.	**56**
Split the smaller number into **tens** and **units**.	**30** and **4**
Add the **tens** to the bigger number...	**56 + 30 = 86**
... then add the **units** to get the answer.	**86 + 4 = 90**

Split the smaller number inside the dashed box and fill in the white boxes to work out the answer.

31 + 15 ⇨ 15 → 10 / 5 ⇨ 31 + 10 = 41 ⇨ 41 + 5 = ☐

22 + 63 ⇨ 22 → 20 / 2 ⇨ ☐ + ☐ = ☐ ⇨ ☐ + ☐ = ☐

18 + 76 ⇨ 18 → ☐ / ☐ ⇨ ☐ + ☐ = ☐ ⇨ ☐ + ☐ = ☐

69 + 39 ⇨ ☐ → ☐ / ☐ ⇨ ☐ + ☐ = ☐ ⇨ ☐ + ☐ = ☐

Do each question in your head and write your answer in the red box. Jot down numbers in the space if you need to.

14 + 23 =
37

43 + 41 =

56 + 13 =

88 + 21 =

92 + 47 =

52 + 73 =

650 + 49 =

807 + 73 =

Answer the questions below.

Add sixty-two to seventeen.   79

What is fifty plus thirty-three?

What do you get when you add fifty-two to ninety-five?

What is twenty-nine add thirty-eight?

What is the total of sixty-five and fifty-seven?

What is the sum of seventy-eight and forty-two?

Write the answers to the questions below.
See how quickly you can get them all right.

7	+	2	=	9	14	+	77	=	
5	+	6	=		41	+	49	=	
6	+	9	=		38	+	39	=	
12	+	8	=		61	+	27	=	
36	+	2	=		58	+	21	=	
6	+	30	=		16	+	80	=	
91	+	8	=		29	+	19	=	
9	+	34	=		13	+	400	=	
25	+	7	=		510	+	200	=	
10	+	60	=		21	+	301	=	
41	+	46	=		230	+	70	=	
32	+	34	=		604	+	280	=	
12	+	67	=		270	+	700	=	
63	+	48	=		507	+	100	=	
87	+	31	=		45	+	2020	=	
25	+	75	=		1500	+	120	=	
44	+	98	=		4060	+	200	=	
17	+	84	=		600	+	270	=	

Subtraction

Subtracting numbers in your head can be tricky.
Splitting them up can make it easier.

Here's an example: **86 – 29 = ?**

Keep the bigger number whole.	**86**
Split the smaller number into **tens** and **units**.	**20** and **9**
Subtract the **tens** from the bigger number...	**86 – 20 = 66**
... then subtract the **units** to get the answer.	**66 – 9 = 57**

Split the smaller number inside the dashed box and fill in the white boxes to work out the answer.

27 – 12 ⟹ 12 → 10 / 2 ⟹ 27 – 10 = 17 ⟹ 17 – 2 = ☐

42 – 35 ⟹ 35 → 30 / 5 ⟹ ☐ – ☐ = ☐ ⟹ ☐ – ☐ = ☐

76 – 41 ⟹ ☐ → ☐ / ☐ ⟹ ☐ – ☐ = ☐ ⟹ ☐ – ☐ = ☐

55 – 26 ⟹ ☐ → ☐ / ☐ ⟹ ☐ – ☐ = ☐ ⟹ ☐ – ☐ = ☐

Do each question in your head and write your answer in the green box. Jot down numbers in the space if you need to.

55 − 32 =
23

57 − 22 =

26 − 14 =

74 − 43 =

62 − 47 =

86 − 48 =

95 − 53 =

89 − 35 =

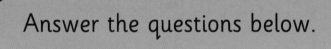

Answer the questions below.

Take away twenty-two from forty-four.   22

What is fifty-six minus twenty-one?

What do you get when you subtract forty-six from eighty?

What is thirty-seven minus twenty-eight?

What is the difference between seventy-five and sixty-two?

Subtract twenty-three from sixty-four.

Write the answers to the questions below.
See how quickly you can get them all right.

8 – 6 =	2	26 – 18 =
9 – 4 =		33 – 26 =
10 – 7 =		81 – 63 =
25 – 4 =		72 – 57 =
30 – 8 =		35 – 22 =
69 – 9 =		90 – 85 =
49 – 6 =		97 – 79 =
33 – 6 =		900 – 350 =
74 – 7 =		600 – 56 =
32 – 21 =		752 – 400 =
57 – 36 =		300 – 19 =
88 – 75 =		820 – 40 =
67 – 49 =		306 – 103 =
98 – 53 =		961 – 205 =
52 – 46 =		5000 – 400 =
86 – 25 =		5660 – 240 =
75 – 66 =		8086 – 65 =
99 – 88 =		7990 – 1030 =

Checking & Estimating

Subtracting is the opposite of adding. This means that if you know one calculation you can work out others. Here's an example:

$$10 + 7 = 17$$ so $17 - 7 = 10$
and $17 - 10 = 7$

Working out the opposite of a calculation is useful for checking your answer is right.

Work out the two opposite calculations to each addition on the left. Write your answers in the boxes.

$$23 + 12 = 35$$

$$35 - 23 = 12$$

$$34 + 6 = 40$$

Check these calculations by filling in the missing boxes.

$$16 + 15 = 31 \Rightarrow 31 - \boxed{} = 16$$

$$41 + 29 = 70 \Rightarrow \boxed{} - 29 = 41$$

$$260 + 120 = 380 \Rightarrow 380 - 120 = \boxed{}$$

You can also check your calculations by rounding your numbers to estimate the answer.
Here's an example: **207 + 490 = 697**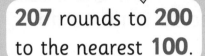

207 rounds to **200** to the nearest **100**.

490 rounds to **500** to the nearest **100**.

200 + 500 = 700, so the answer seems about right.

Round these numbers to the nearest 10.

74 ⇨ 70   63 ⇨ ☐   17 ⇨ ☐   98 ⇨ ☐

By rounding each number to the nearest 10,
decide whether you think each calculation could be correct.

37 + 618 = 655

Could this be correct?

✓ Yes   ☐ No

381 + 27 = 462

Could this be correct?

☐ Yes   ☐ No

196 + 83 = 279

Could this be correct?

☐ Yes   ☐ No

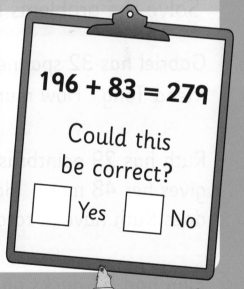

By rounding each number to the nearest 100,
estimate the answer to each calculation.

508 + 205 is roughly ☐.   177 + 298 is roughly ☐.

412 + 384 is roughly ☐.   681 + 320 is roughly ☐.

Problem Solving

Some maths questions won't tell you whether you need to add or subtract. You'll need to decide what to do. Here's an example:

Jayden buys some bouncy balls. He loses **28**, and has **32** left. **How many did he start with?**

You're given two numbers...

... and asked what the total is.

Add together the two numbers:

28 + 32 = 60

Solve the problems below and write the answers in the boxes.

Gabriel has 32 spanners. He sells 12 of them to his friend Tony. How many does he keep for himself?

20

Ruth has 29 paintbrushes. Her friend Josie gives her 48 more. How many paintbrushes does Ruth have in total?

Finn had 57 ducks on his farm. Some new ducklings hatched. Finn now has 72 ducks. How many ducklings hatched?

Josh has 24 oranges, 20 lemons and 10 apples. How many pieces of fruit does he have altogether?

Use the menu for Janice's Tearoom to answer the questions. Write the answer in the boxes.

Janice's Tearoom

Tea	45p
Coffee	50p
Flapjack	35p
Muffin	40p
Scone	55p

How much does it cost to buy a cup of tea and a scone?

£ [1]

If you have 85p and you buy a coffee, what else can you buy?

[ ]

Kerry has 95p. She buys a cup of tea and a muffin. How much change does she get?

[ ] p

Atis would like to buy a coffee and a muffin but he only has 80p. How much more money does he need?

[ ] p

Work out the answers to these problems.

Olivia has 2 pieces of rope. One piece is 42 m long and the other piece is 39 m long. What is the total length of Olivia's ropes?

[ ] m

Dayna has 120 sweets. 54 are red and the rest are orange. How many sweets are orange?

[ ]

Fred is playing golf. He brought 200 golf balls with him and has lost 86. How many does he have left?

[ ]

Nadia has £17. She gets £7 for her birthday. How much more money does she need to buy a jumper which costs £27?

£ [ ]

Mike has 300 sunflower seeds and 150 carrot seeds. He gives away 30 seeds. How many seeds does he have left?

[ ]

Multiplying & Dividing by 10 and 100

When you multiply by 10, the digits move one space to the left along the place value columns.

H	T	U
		4
× 100		
= 4	0	0

When you multiply by 100, the digits move two spaces to the left.

H	T	U
	8	9
× 10		
= 8	9	0

Fill in these boxes to complete the calculations.

7	×	100	=	700		9	×	10	=	
23	×	10	=			65	×	10	=	
8	×	100	=			33	×	100	=	

A shop sells chocolates in boxes of 10 and sweets in jars of 100. Answer the questions below.

Kirstie buys 12 jars of sweets.
How many sweets does she have?

Logan buys 15 boxes of chocolates.
How many chocolates does he have?

Cathleen buys 42 jars of sweets.
How many sweets does she have?

Practise and Learn

Mental Maths

Ages 7-9

Answers

This section shows each of the pages from the book with the answers filled in.

The pages are laid out in the same way as the book itself, so the questions can be easily marked by you, or by your child.

There are also helpful learning tips with some of the pages.

4

Adding & Subtracting 1s, 10s, 100s ...

You can add and subtract by counting on in ones, tens, hundreds or thousands. Here are some examples:

628 + 3 = 628 $\xrightarrow{+1}$ 629 $\xrightarrow{+1}$ 630 $\xrightarrow{+1}$ 631

110 – 20 = 110 $\xrightarrow{-10}$ 100 $\xrightarrow{-10}$ 90

120 + 200 = 120 $\xrightarrow{+100}$ 220 $\xrightarrow{+100}$ 320

3700 – 1000 = 3700 $\xrightarrow{-1000}$ 2700

Complete the additions and write the answers in the boxes.

100 + 5 = **105**	520 + 9 = **529**
231 + 60 = **291**	378 + 20 = **398**
149 + 300 = **449**	645 + 200 = **845**

Complete the subtractions and write the answers in the boxes.

288 – 6 = **282**	323 – 3 = **320**
969 – 20 = **949**	561 – 40 = **521**
540 – 500 = **40**	765 – 600 = **165**

4

5

Write the answers to the calculations in the circles.

20 $\xrightarrow{+40}$ 60 $\xrightarrow{-30}$ 30 $\xrightarrow{+10}$ 40 $\xrightarrow{+20}$ 60

20 $\xleftarrow{-30}$ 50 $\xleftarrow{-20}$ 70 $\xleftarrow{+40}$ 30 $\xleftarrow{-30}$

Write the missing numbers in the boxes.

370 (–70) **300** | 112 (+50) **162** | 603 (–40) **563**

591 (–60) **531** | 226 (+70) **296** | 894 (–40) **854**

460 (+50) **510** | 765 (+20) **785** | 910 (–60) **850**

Fill in the empty boxes to complete each calculation.

230 $\xrightarrow{+100}$ 330	550 $\xrightarrow{-300}$ **250**	403 $\xrightarrow{+200}$ **603**
820 $\xrightarrow{-400}$ **420**	109 $\xrightarrow{+600}$ **709**	380 $\xrightarrow{-100}$ **280**

2500 $\xrightarrow{+2000}$ **4500**	7800 $\xrightarrow{-3000}$ **4800**
9067 $\xrightarrow{-4000}$ **5067**	3303 $\xrightarrow{+6000}$ **9303**

5

Addition

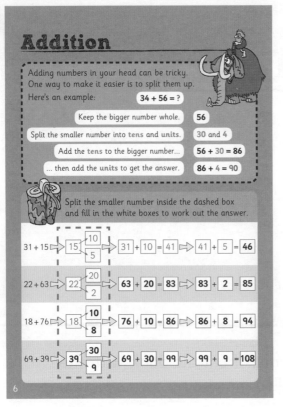

Adding numbers in your head can be tricky. One way to make it easier is to split them up. Here's an example:

34 + 56 = ?

Keep the bigger number whole.	**56**
Split the smaller number into **tens** and **units**.	**30 and 4**
Add the **tens** to the bigger number...	**56 + 30 = 86**
... then add the **units** to get the answer.	**86 + 4 = 90**

Split the smaller number inside the dashed box and fill in the white boxes to work out the answer.

31 + 15 ⇨ 15 [10 / 5] ⇨ 31 + 10 = 41 ⇨ 41 + 5 = **46**

22 + 63 ⇨ 22 [20 / 2] ⇨ 63 + 20 = 83 ⇨ 83 + 2 = **85**

18 + 76 ⇨ 18 [**10** / **8**] ⇨ 76 + 10 = 86 ⇨ 86 + 8 = **94**

69 + 39 ⇨ 39 [**30** / **9**] ⇨ 69 + 30 = 99 ⇨ 99 + 9 = **108**

6

If your child is struggling with the splitting method, help them to identify the tens and units for each number they need to split.

Do each question in your head and write your answer in the red box. Jot down numbers in the space if you need to.

14 + 23 = [37]　　43 + 41 = [84]

56 + 13 = [69]　　88 + 21 = [109]

92 + 47 = [139]　　52 + 73 = [125]

650 + 49 = [699]　　807 + 73 = [880]

Answer the questions below.

Add sixty-two to seventeen.	79
What is fifty plus thirty-three?	**83**
What do you get when you add fifty-two to ninety-five?	**147**
What is twenty-nine add thirty-eight?	**67**
What is the total of sixty-five and fifty-seven?	**122**
What is the sum of seventy-eight and forty-two?	**120**

7

Write the answers to the questions below. See how quickly you can get them all right.

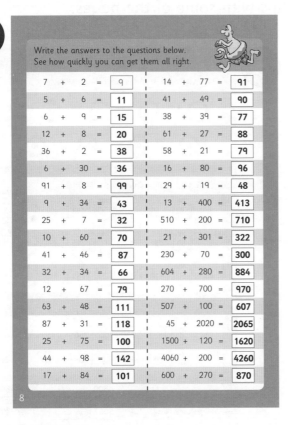

7	+	2	=	9		14	+	77	=	91
5	+	6	=	11		41	+	49	=	90
6	+	9	=	15		38	+	39	=	77
12	+	8	=	20		61	+	27	=	88
36	+	2	=	38		58	+	21	=	79
6	+	30	=	36		16	+	80	=	96
91	+	8	=	99		29	+	19	=	48
9	+	34	=	43		13	+	400	=	413
25	+	7	=	32		510	+	200	=	710
10	+	60	=	70		21	+	301	=	322
41	+	46	=	87		230	+	70	=	300
32	+	34	=	66		604	+	280	=	884
12	+	67	=	79		270	+	700	=	970
63	+	48	=	111		507	+	100	=	607
87	+	31	=	118		45	+	2020	=	2065
25	+	75	=	100		1500	+	120	=	1620
44	+	98	=	142		4060	+	200	=	4260
17	+	84	=	101		600	+	270	=	870

8

Subtraction

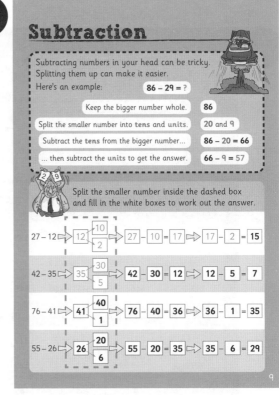

Subtracting numbers in your head can be tricky. Splitting them up can make it easier. Here's an example:

86 – 29 = ?

Keep the bigger number whole.	**86**
Split the smaller number into **tens** and **units**.	**20 and 9**
Subtract the **tens** from the bigger number...	**86 – 20 = 66**
... then subtract the **units** to get the answer.	**66 – 9 = 57**

Split the smaller number inside the dashed box and fill in the white boxes to work out the answer.

27 – 12 ⇨ 12 [10 / 2] ⇨ 27 – 10 = 17 ⇨ 17 – 2 = **15**

42 – 35 ⇨ 35 [30 / 5] ⇨ 42 – 30 = 12 ⇨ 12 – 5 = **7**

76 – 41 ⇨ 41 [**40** / **1**] ⇨ 76 – 40 = 36 ⇨ 36 – 1 = **35**

55 – 26 ⇨ 26 [**20** / **6**] ⇨ 55 – 20 = 35 ⇨ 35 – 6 = **29**

9

Do each question in your head and write your answer in the green box. Jot down numbers in the space if you need to.

55 − 32 =	23	
57 − 22 =		35
26 − 14 =	12	
74 − 43 =		31
62 − 47 =	15	
86 − 48 =		38
95 − 53 =	42	
89 − 35 =		54

Answer the questions below.

Take away twenty-two from forty-four.	22
What is fifty-six minus twenty-one?	35
What do you get when you subtract forty-six from eighty?	34
What is thirty-seven minus twenty-eight?	9
What is the difference between seventy-five and sixty-two?	13
Subtract twenty-three from sixty-four.	41

Write the answers to the questions below. See how quickly you can get them all right.

8	−	6	=	2	26 − 18 =		8
9	−	4	=	5	33 − 26 =		7
10	−	7	=	3	81 − 63 =		18
25	−	4	=	21	72 − 57 =		15
30	−	8	=	22	35 − 22 =		13
69	−	9	=	60	90 − 85 =		5
49	−	6	=	43	97 − 79 =		18
33	−	6	=	27	900 − 350 =		550
74	−	7	=	67	600 − 56 =		544
32	−	21	=	11	752 − 400 =		352
57	−	36	=	21	300 − 19 =		281
88	−	75	=	13	820 − 40 =		780
67	−	49	=	18	306 − 103 =		203
98	−	53	=	45	961 − 205 =		756
52	−	46	=	6	5000 − 400 =		4600
86	−	25	=	61	5660 − 240 =		5420
75	−	66	=	9	8086 − 65 =		8021
99	−	88	=	11	7990 − 1030 =		6960

Encourage your child to work out the answers to these questions in their head. They can jot numbers down, but they mustn't do any written working out.

Checking & Estimating

Subtracting is the opposite of adding. This means that if you know one calculation you can work out others. Here's an example:

$10 + 7 = 17$ ⟹ so $17 − 7 = 10$ and $17 − 10 = 7$

Working out the opposite of a calculation is useful for checking your answer is right.

Work out the two opposite calculations to each addition on the left. Write your answers in the boxes.

$23 + 12 = 35$ ⟹ $35 − 23 = 12$
$35 − 12 = 23$

$34 + 6 = 40$ ⟹ $40 − 34 = 6$
$40 − 6 = 34$

Check these calculations by filling in the missing boxes.

$16 + 15 = 31$ ⟹ $31 − 15 = 16$

$41 + 29 = 70$ ⟹ $70 − 29 = 41$

$260 + 120 = 380$ ⟹ $380 − 120 = 260$

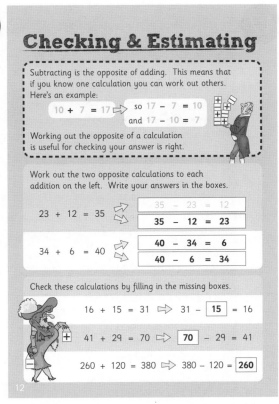

You can also check your calculations by rounding your numbers to estimate the answer. Here's an example: $207 + 490 = 697$

207 rounds to 200 to the nearest 100.
490 rounds to 500 to the nearest 100.

$200 + 500 = 700$, so the answer seems about right.

Round these numbers to the nearest 10.

74 ⟹ 70   63 ⟹ 60   17 ⟹ 20   98 ⟹ 100

By rounding each number to the nearest 10, decide whether you think each calculation could be correct.

$37 + 618 = 655$
Could this be correct?
✓ Yes ☐ No

$381 + 27 = 462$
Could this be correct?
☐ Yes ✓ No

$196 + 83 = 279$
Could this be correct?
✓ Yes ☐ No

By rounding each number to the nearest 100, estimate the answer to each calculation.

508 + 205 is roughly 700.   177 + 298 is roughly 500.

412 + 384 is roughly 800.   681 + 320 is roughly 1000.

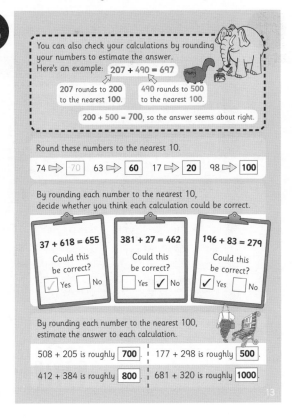

As an extension exercise, ask your child to use these techniques to check their answers on the addition and subtraction pages.

Problem Solving

Some maths questions won't tell you whether you need to add or subtract. You'll need to decide what to do. Here's an example:

Jayden buys some bouncy balls. He loses **28**, and has **32** left. How many did he start with?

You're given two numbers...

... and asked what the total is.

Add together the two numbers: **28 + 32 = 60**

Solve the problems below and write the answers in the boxes.

Gabriel has 32 spanners. He sells 12 of them to his friend Tony. How many does he keep for himself? **20**

Ruth has 29 paintbrushes. Her friend Josie gives her 48 more. How many paintbrushes does Ruth have in total? **77**

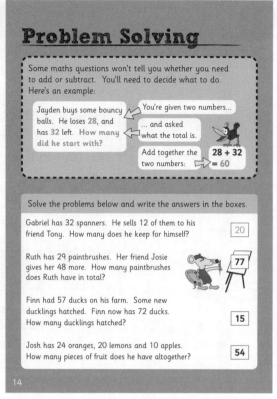

Finn had 57 ducks on his farm. Some new ducklings hatched. Finn now has 72 ducks. How many ducklings hatched? **15**

Josh has 24 oranges, 20 lemons and 10 apples. How many pieces of fruit does he have altogether? **54**

Your child might struggle to work out whether the question is asking them to add or subtract. You can help them by working through some examples together.

Use the menu for Janice's Tearoom to answer the questions. Write the answer in the boxes.

Janice's Tearoom
Tea 45p
Coffee 50p
Flapjack 35p
Muffin 40p
Scone 55p

How much does it cost to buy a cup of tea and a scone? £ **1**

If you have 85p and you buy a coffee, what else can you buy? **a flapjack**

Kerry has 95p. She buys a cup of tea and a muffin. How much change does she get? **10** p

Atis would like to buy a coffee and a muffin but he only has 80p. How much more money does he need? **10** p

Work out the answers to these problems.

Olivia has 2 pieces of rope. One piece is 42 m long and the other piece is 39 m long. What is the total length of Olivia's ropes? **81** m

Dayna has 120 sweets. 54 are red and the rest are orange. How many sweets are orange? **66**

Fred is playing golf. He brought 200 golf balls with him and has lost 86. How many does he have left? **114**

Nadia has £17. She gets £7 for her birthday. How much more money does she need to buy a jumper which costs £27? £ **3**

Mike has 300 sunflower seeds and 150 carrot seeds. He gives away 30 seeds. How many seeds does he have left? **420**

Multiplying & Dividing by 10 and 100

When you multiply by 10, the digits move one space to the left along the place value columns.

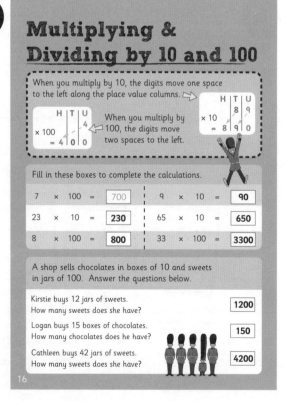

When you multiply by 100, the digits move two spaces to the left.

Fill in these boxes to complete the calculations.

7 × 100 = **700**   9 × 10 = **90**

23 × 10 = **230**   65 × 10 = **650**

8 × 100 = **800**   33 × 100 = **3300**

A shop sells chocolates in boxes of 10 and sweets in jars of 100. Answer the questions below.

Kirstie buys 12 jars of sweets. How many sweets does she have? **1200**

Logan buys 15 boxes of chocolates. How many chocolates does he have? **150**

Cathleen buys 42 jars of sweets. How many sweets does she have? **4200**

When you divide by 10, move the digits one place to the right. 5 ÷ 10 = **0.5**

When you divide by 100, move the digits two places to the right.

tenths   hundredths

Fill in these boxes to complete the calculations.

65 ÷ 10 = **6.5**   50 ÷ 100 = **0.5**

800 ÷ 100 = **8**   27 ÷ 10 = **2.7**

31 ÷ 100 = **0.31**   980 ÷ 10 = **98**

92 ÷ 10 = **9.2**   72 ÷ 100 = **0.72**

Use division to solve the problems below.

Jenny owns 450 teapots. If she cleans 10 each day, how many days will it take her to clean all of them? **45** days

Lukas makes 10 apple pies from 2 kg of apples. How many kilograms of apple are there in each pie? **0.2** kg

Frank buys 100 flowers for £8. How much did each flower cost? £ **0.08**

Micaela divides 45 litres of orange juice between 100 glasses. How much does each glass have? **0.45** litres

If your child finds it hard to split numbers into place value columns, help them to identify the tens, units, tenths and hundredths of each number.

Doubling & Halving

Doubling is the same as multiplying by 2. Split the number into tens and units to help you. ➤ Double 36

Split 36 into tens and units.	30 and 6
Multiply the tens and units by 2.	30 × 2 = 60 and 6 × 2 = 12
Then add these numbers together.	60 + 12 = 72

Complete each chain using the instructions.

5 → doubled → 10 → doubled → **20** → doubled → **40**

6 → doubled → **12** → doubled → **24** → doubled → **48**

8 → doubled → **16** → doubled → **32** → doubled → **64**

7 → doubled → **14** → doubled → **28** → doubled → **56**

Double each number and write the answer in the box.

4 ➤ 8	33 ➤ **66**	13 ➤ **26**
9 ➤ **18**	42 ➤ **84**	25 ➤ **50**
11 ➤ **22**	19 ➤ **38**	37 ➤ **74**
29 ➤ **58**	50 ➤ **100**	46 ➤ **92**

When you halve a number you divide it by 2. Splitting numbers also helps you to halve them. ➤ Halve 36

Split 36 into tens and units.	30 and 6
Divide the tens and units by 2.	30 ÷ 2 = 15 and 6 ÷ 2 = 3
Then add these numbers together.	15 + 3 = 18

Complete each chain using the instructions.

8 → halved → 4 → halved → **2** → halved → **1**

40 → halved → **20** → halved → **10** → halved → **5**

24 → halved → **12** → halved → **6** → halved → **3**

56 → halved → **28** → halved → **14** → halved → **7**

Halve each number and write the answer in the box.

6 ➤ 3	18 ➤ **9**	32 ➤ **16**
42 ➤ **21**	16 ➤ **8**	34 ➤ **17**
22 ➤ **11**	26 ➤ **13**	64 ➤ **32**
44 ➤ **22**	46 ➤ **23**	38 ➤ **19**
62 ➤ **31**	58 ➤ **29**	54 ➤ **27**

Multiplication

You can do some multiplications just by knowing your times tables. Here's an example.

4 boxes each contain 8 cups. How many cups are there in total?

This is the same as asking: 4 × 8 = ?

You know that **4 × 8 = 32**, so there are 32 cups in total.

The times tables are at the back of the book if you need them.

Draw lines to match the calculations below with their answers.

5 × 7 → 36

8 × 10 → 63 → 7 × 9

3 × 12 → 60 → 12 × 5

80 → 35

0 → 0 × 3

Answer the questions below using your times tables.

What is three multiplied by six?	**18**
What do you multiply by five to get forty?	**8**
What is four multiplied by itself?	**16**
How many eights make eighty-eight?	**11**
What is seven multiplied by six?	**42**

Answer the questions below using your times tables.

Jackie buys 3 packs of dog food. Each pack has 7 tins. How many tins does she buy in total?	**21**
It takes Ben 4 hours to make a model aeroplane. How many hours does it take him to make 9 model aeroplanes?	**36**
A bakery sells sausage rolls in boxes of 12. If Dave buys 4 boxes, how many sausage rolls does he have?	**48**
Samira wants to give 7 stickers to each of her 8 friends. How many stickers does she need in total?	**56**
Tim's bookcase has 5 shelves. He can fit 11 books on each shelf. How many books will fit on the bookcase?	**55**

Work out how much it would cost to buy different numbers of items and write the answers in the boxes.

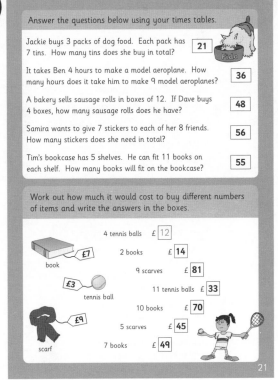

book **£7**

tennis ball **£3**

scarf **£9**

4 tennis balls	£ 12
2 books	£ **14**
9 scarves	£ **81**
11 tennis balls	£ **33**
10 books	£ **70**
5 scarves	£ **45**
7 books	£ **49**

If your child finds these pages difficult, make sure they have a good grasp of the times tables. It will make it easier (and quicker) to do multiplication mentally.

Write the answers to the questions below.
See how fast you can do them all.

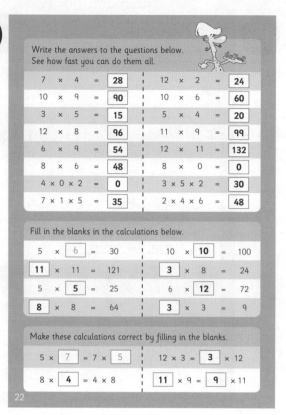

7	×	4	=	**28**	12	×	2	=	**24**
10	×	9	=	**90**	10	×	6	=	**60**
3	×	5	=	**15**	5	×	4	=	**20**
12	×	8	=	**96**	11	×	9	=	**99**
6	×	9	=	**54**	12	×	11	=	**132**
8	×	6	=	**48**	8	×	0	=	**0**
4 × 0 × 2			=	**0**	3 × 5 × 2			=	**30**
7 × 1 × 5			=	**35**	2 × 4 × 6			=	**48**

Fill in the blanks in the calculations below.

5 × **6** = 30   10 × **10** = 100

11 × 11 = 121   **3** × 8 = 24

5 × **5** = 25   6 × **12** = 72

8 × 8 = 64   **3** × 3 = 9

Make these calculations correct by filling in the blanks.

5 × **7** = 7 × **5**   12 × 3 = **3** × 12

8 × **4** = 4 × 8   **11** × 9 = **9** × 11

Division

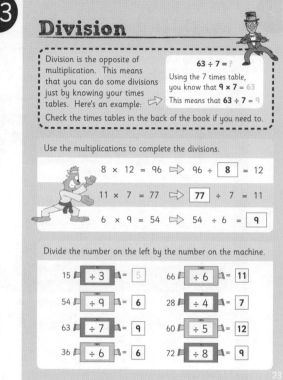

Division is the opposite of multiplication. This means that you can do some divisions just by knowing your times tables. Here's an example:

63 ÷ 7 = ?
Using the 7 times table, you know that **9 × 7** = 63
This means that **63 ÷ 7** = 9

Check the times tables in the back of the book if you need to.

Use the multiplications to complete the divisions.

8 × 12 = 96 ⇨ 96 ÷ **8** = 12

11 × 7 = 77 ⇨ **77** ÷ 7 = 11

6 × 9 = 54 ⇨ 54 ÷ 6 = **9**

Divide the number on the left by the number on the machine.

15 ÷ 3 = 5   66 ÷ 6 = **11**

54 ÷ 9 = **6**   28 ÷ 4 = **7**

63 ÷ 7 = **9**   60 ÷ 5 = **12**

36 ÷ 6 = **6**   72 ÷ 8 = **9**

Match up the calculations below with their correct answers.

72 ÷ 12   10   8   100 ÷ 1

45 ÷ 9   6   56 ÷ 7

30 ÷ 3   5   100   4   32 ÷ 8

Answer the questions below using your times tables.

What is seventy divided by ten?   **7**

What divided by 3 gives 4?   **12**

What is fifty-five divided by eleven?   **5**

What is 72 divided by 9?   **8**

Answer the questions below using your times tables.

A bus has 16 seats. The seats are in rows of 4.
How many rows of seats are there on the bus?   **4**

Jill divides 56 people into 8 teams.
How many people are in each team?   **7**

Each guest at a party is given 3 sweets. If 36 sweets
are given out, how many guests must there be?   **12**

Jackson is moving 121 cars. He can fit 11
cars on each lorry. How many lorries are
needed to move all of the cars at once?   **11**

Write the answers to the questions below.
See how quickly you can get them all right.

9	÷	3	=	3	90	÷	10	=	**9**
8	÷	4	=	**2**	36	÷	4	=	**9**
6	÷	1	=	**6**	48	÷	12	=	**4**
12	÷	4	=	**3**	81	÷	9	=	**9**
16	÷	8	=	**2**	49	÷	7	=	**7**
20	÷	4	=	**5**	64	÷	8	=	**8**
21	÷	7	=	**3**	45	÷	9	=	**5**
18	÷	3	=	**6**	77	÷	11	=	**7**
20	÷	2	=	**10**	60	÷	12	=	**5**
30	÷	6	=	**5**	72	÷	6	=	**12**
110	÷	10	=	**11**	108	÷	12	=	**9**
48	÷	6	=	**8**	63	÷	9	=	**7**

Fill in the blanks in the calculations below.

24 ÷ 4 = 6   **21** ÷ 3 = 7

42 ÷ 7 = 6   144 ÷ **12** = 12

80 ÷ **10** = 8   **11** ÷ 11 = 1

88 ÷ 8 = 11   48 ÷ **8** = 6

If your child finds division tricky, remind
them that it is the inverse of multiplication.
Knowing their times tables will also help.

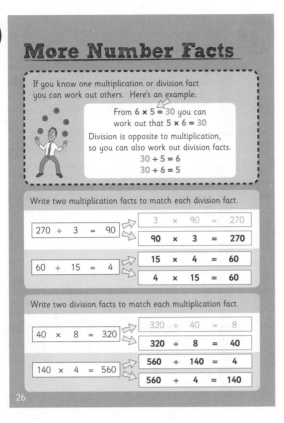

26 — More Number Facts

If you know one multiplication or division fact you can work out others. Here's an example:

From 6 × 5 = 30 you can work out that 5 × 6 = 30

Division is opposite to multiplication, so you can also work out division facts.
30 ÷ 5 = 6
30 ÷ 6 = 5

Write two multiplication facts to match each division fact.

270 ÷ 3 = 90 →
3 × 90 = 270
90 × 3 = 270

60 ÷ 15 = 4 →
15 × 4 = 60
4 × 15 = 60

Write two division facts to match each multiplication fact.

40 × 8 = 320 →
320 ÷ 40 = 8
320 ÷ 8 = 40

140 × 4 = 560 →
560 ÷ 140 = 4
560 ÷ 4 = 140

26

27

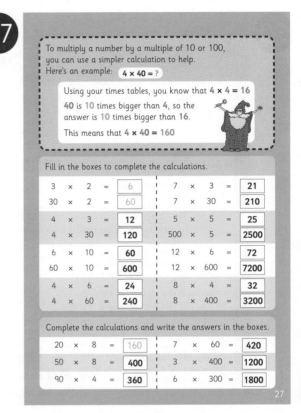

To multiply a number by a multiple of 10 or 100, you can use a simpler calculation to help.
Here's an example: 4 × 40 = ?

Using your times tables, you know that 4 × 4 = 16

40 is 10 times bigger than 4, so the answer is 10 times bigger than 16.

This means that 4 × 40 = 160

Fill in the boxes to complete the calculations.

3 × 2 = 6			7 × 3 = 21
30 × 2 = 60			7 × 30 = 210
4 × 3 = 12			5 × 5 = 25
4 × 30 = 120			500 × 5 = 2500
6 × 10 = 60			12 × 6 = 72
60 × 10 = 600			12 × 600 = 7200
4 × 6 = 24			8 × 4 = 32
4 × 60 = 240			8 × 400 = 3200

Complete the calculations and write the answers in the boxes.

20 × 8 = 160		7 × 60 = 420
50 × 8 = 400		3 × 400 = 1200
90 × 4 = 360		6 × 300 = 1800

27

28 — Problem Solving

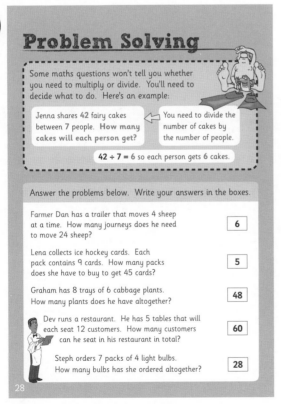

Some maths questions won't tell you whether you need to multiply or divide. You'll need to decide what to do. Here's an example:

Jenna shares 42 fairy cakes between 7 people. **How many cakes will each person get?** ← You need to divide the number of cakes by the number of people.

42 ÷ 7 = 6 so each person gets 6 cakes.

Answer the problems below. Write your answers in the boxes.

Farmer Dan has a trailer that moves 4 sheep at a time. How many journeys does he need to move 24 sheep? **6**

Lena collects ice hockey cards. Each pack contains 9 cards. How many packs does she have to buy to get 45 cards? **5**

Graham has 8 trays of 6 cabbage plants. How many plants does he have altogether? **48**

Dev runs a restaurant. He has 5 tables that will each seat 12 customers. How many customers can he seat in his restaurant in total? **60**

Steph orders 7 packs of 4 light bulbs. How many bulbs has she ordered altogether? **28**

28

29

Work out the answers to these problems.

Grant has 3 types of fish in his pond. He has 8 of each type. In total, how many fish does he have? **24**

A bag of sweets costs 36p. A chocolate bar costs half as much. How much does the chocolate bar cost? **18** p

Anna buys 66 items in a shop. She wants to split the shopping equally into 6 shopping bags. How many items should she put in each bag? **11**

There are 36 people travelling on a train with 3 carriages. Each carriage has the same number of people. How many people are there in each carriage? **12**

James buys a set of 7 books. It costs £21. How much does each book cost? £ **3**

There are 26 children in a class. Half of them are girls. How many girls are there? **13**

There are 72 people staying on a campsite. Each tent holds 6 people. How many tents are there in total? **12**

Attila has 5 shirts and 4 ties. How many different shirt and tie combinations can he wear? **20**

It costs £4 to buy 2 ice creams. How much does it cost to buy 6 ice creams? £ **12**

29

If your child struggles with word problems, help them pick out the important information in each question and explain what to do with it.

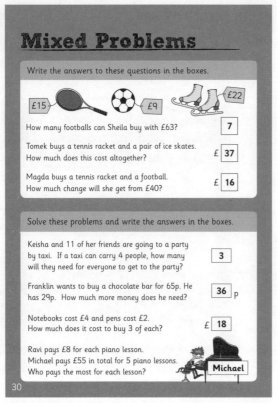

Mixed Problems

30

Write the answers to these questions in the boxes.

£15 · ⚽ £9 · £22

How many footballs can Sheila buy with £63? **7**

Tomek buys a tennis racket and a pair of ice skates. How much does this cost altogether? £ **37**

Magda buys a tennis racket and a football. How much change will she get from £40? £ **16**

Solve these problems and write the answers in the boxes.

Keisha and 11 of her friends are going to a party by taxi. If a taxi can carry 4 people, how many will they need for everyone to get to the party? **3**

Franklin wants to buy a chocolate bar for 65p. He has 29p. How much more money does he need? **36** p

Notebooks cost £4 and pens cost £2. How much does it cost to buy 3 of each? £ **18**

Ravi pays £8 for each piano lesson. Michael pays £55 in total for 5 piano lessons. Who pays the most for each lesson? **Michael**

30

31

Here are some more problems to work out in your head. Write the answers in the boxes.

A shop has exactly 50 customers every day. How many do they have in 6 days? **300**

One hen lays 6 eggs each week. Another hen lays 4 eggs each week. How many eggs will they lay in total in 5 weeks? **50**

One spaceship can hold 8 aliens. If there are 48 aliens, how many spaceships are needed to carry them all? **6**

Lottie buys 20 carrots, 40 potatoes and 25 tomatoes. How many items has she bought altogether? **85**

Pardeep and his 3 friends each bake 12 cakes. How many cakes do they bake in total? **48**

It takes Luke 30 minutes to mow the lawn and 4 times as long to wash the windows. How many minutes does it take him to wash the windows? **120**

A shop sells bracelets for £4 and necklaces for £3. How much would two sets of bracelets and necklaces cost? £ **14**

31

Encourage your child to read each problem carefully so they are confident about what they need to do.

Elephants and Monkeys

You'll need a counter for each player and a dice. Place your counters on the first square, and take it in turns to roll the dice once. Follow the instructions when you land on them.

FINISH

18 · 9 · 96

100

42 · 12

75 · 119

START · 78

When you divide by 10, move the digits one place to the right.

$5 \div 10 = \mathbf{0.5}$

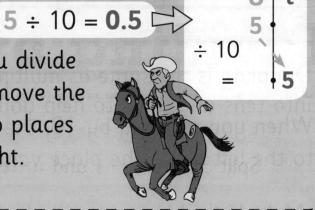

T	U	t	h
8	4		

$\div 100$ =

| | 0 | 8 | 4 |

tenths — hundredths

When you divide by 100, move the digits two places to the right.

Fill in these boxes to complete the calculations.

65	÷	10	=	6.5		50	÷	100	=	
800	÷	100	=			27	÷	10	=	
31	÷	100	=			980	÷	10	=	
92	÷	10	=			72	÷	100	=	

Use division to solve the problems below.

Jenny owns 450 teapots. If she cleans 10 each day, how many days will it take her to clean all of them?

 days

Lukas makes 10 apple pies from 2 kg of apples. How many kilograms of apple are there in each pie?

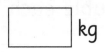 kg

Frank buys 100 flowers for £8. How much did each flower cost?

£

Micaela divides 45 litres of orange juice between 100 glasses. How much does each glass have?

 litres

Doubling & Halving

Doubling is the same as multiplying by 2. Split the number into tens and units to help you.

Double 36

Split 36 into **tens** and **units**.	**30** and **6**
Multiply the **tens** and **units** by 2.	$30 \times 2 = 60$ and $6 \times 2 = 12$
Then add these numbers together.	$60 + 12 = 72$

Complete each chain using the instructions.

5 → doubled → 10 → doubled → ☐ → doubled → ☐

6 → doubled → ☐ → doubled → ☐ → doubled → ☐

8 → doubled → ☐ → doubled → ☐ → doubled → ☐

7 → doubled → ☐ → doubled → ☐ → doubled → ☐

Double each number and write the answer in the box.

4 ⇒ 8	33 ⇒ ☐	13 ⇒ ☐
9 ⇒ ☐	42 ⇒ ☐	25 ⇒ ☐
11 ⇒ ☐	19 ⇒ ☐	37 ⇒ ☐
29 ⇒ ☐	50 ⇒ ☐	46 ⇒ ☐

When you halve a number you divide it by 2.
Splitting numbers also helps you to halve them. ⟹ Halve 36

Split 36 into **tens** and **units**.   30 and **6**

Divide the **tens** and **units** by 2.   30 ÷ 2 = 15 and 6 ÷ 2 = **3**

Then add these numbers together.   15 + 3 = **18**

Complete each chain using the instructions.

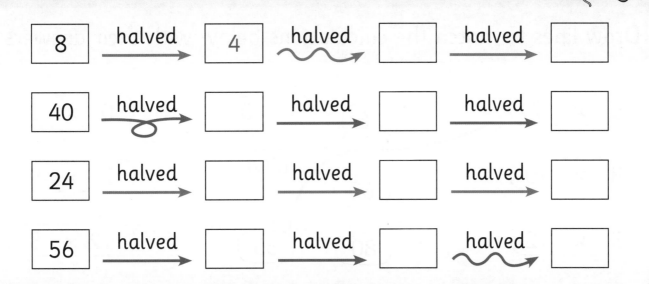

8	halved	4	halved		halved	
40	halved		halved		halved	
24	halved		halved		halved	
56	halved		halved		halved	

Halve each number and write the answer in the box.

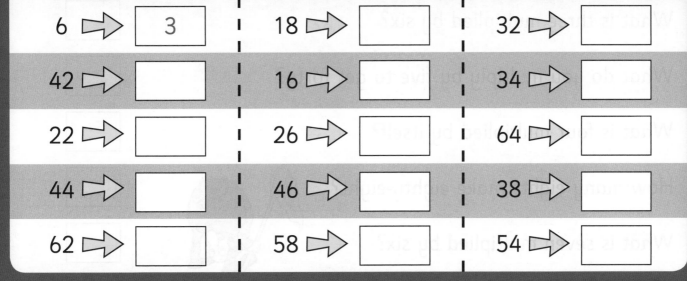

6 ⟹	3	18 ⟹		32 ⟹	
42 ⟹		16 ⟹		34 ⟹	
22 ⟹		26 ⟹		64 ⟹	
44 ⟹		46 ⟹		38 ⟹	
62 ⟹		58 ⟹		54 ⟹	

Multiplication

You can do some multiplications just by knowing your times tables.
Here's an example:

4 boxes each contain **8 cups.**
How many cups are there in total?

This is the same as asking: **4 × 8 = ?**

You know that **4 × 8 = 32**, so there are **32** cups in total.

The times tables are at the back of the book if you need them.

Draw lines to match the calculations below with their answers.

5 × 7	36	0	0 × 3
8 × 10	63		7 × 9
3 × 12	60		12 × 5
	80	35	

Answer the questions below using your times tables.

What is three multiplied by six? ☐

What do you multiply by five to get forty? ☐

What is four multiplied by itself? ☐

How many eights make eighty-eight? ☐

What is seven multiplied by six? ☐

Answer the questions below using your times tables.

Jackie buys 3 packs of dog food. Each pack has 7 tins. How many tins does she buy in total? ☐

It takes Ben 4 hours to make a model aeroplane. How many hours does it take him to make 9 model aeroplanes? ☐

A bakery sells sausage rolls in boxes of 12. If Dave buys 4 boxes, how many sausage rolls does he have? ☐

Samira wants to give 7 stickers to each of her 8 friends. How many stickers does she need in total? ☐

Tim's bookcase has 5 shelves. He can fit 11 books on each shelf. How many books will fit on the bookcase? ☐

Work out how much it would cost to buy different numbers of items and write the answers in the boxes.

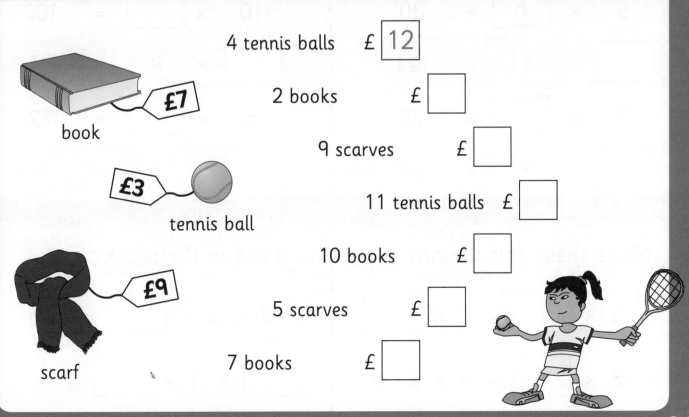

book £7

tennis ball £3

scarf £9

4 tennis balls £ 12

2 books £ ☐

9 scarves £ ☐

11 tennis balls £ ☐

10 books £ ☐

5 scarves £ ☐

7 books £ ☐

Write the answers to the questions below.
See how fast you can do them all.

7	×	4	=			12	×	2	=	
10	×	9	=			10	×	6	=	
3	×	5	=			5	×	4	=	
12	×	8	=			11	×	9	=	
6	×	9	=			12	×	11	=	
8	×	6	=			8	×	0	=	
4 × 0 × 2			=			3 × 5 × 2			=	
7 × 1 × 5			=			2 × 4 × 6			=	

Fill in the blanks in the calculations below.

5	×	6	=	30		10	×		=	100
	×	11	=	121			×	8	=	24
5	×		=	25		6	×		=	72
	×	8	=	64			×	3	=	9

Make these calculations correct by filling in the blanks.

5 × 7 = 7 × 5   12 × 3 = ☐ × 12

8 × ☐ = 4 × 8   ☐ × 9 = ☐ × 11

22

Division

Division is the opposite of multiplication. This means that you can do some divisions just by knowing your times tables. Here's an example:

$63 \div 7 = ?$

Using the 7 times table, you know that $9 \times 7 = 63$

This means that $63 \div 7 = 9$

Check the times tables in the back of the book if you need to.

Use the multiplications to complete the divisions.

$8 \times 12 = 96 \implies 96 \div \boxed{} = 12$

$11 \times 7 = 77 \implies \boxed{} \div 7 = 11$

$6 \times 9 = 54 \implies 54 \div 6 = \boxed{}$

Divide the number on the left by the number on the machine.

15 $\div 3$ = 5

66 $\div 6$ =

54 $\div 9$ =

28 $\div 4$ =

63 $\div 7$ =

60 $\div 5$ =

36 $\div 6$ =

72 $\div 8$ =

Match up the calculations below with their correct answers.

72 ÷ 12   10   8   100 ÷ 1

45 ÷ 9   6   56 ÷ 7
                 5

30 ÷ 3   32 ÷ 8
                 100   4

Answer the questions below using your times tables.

What is seventy divided by ten?

What divided by 3 gives 4?

What is fifty-five divided by eleven?

What is 72 divided by 9?

Answer the questions below using your times tables.

A bus has 16 seats. The seats are in rows of 4.
How many rows of seats are there on the bus?

Jill divides 56 people into 8 teams.
How many people are in each team?

Each guest at a party is given 3 sweets. If 36 sweets
are given out, how many guests must there be?

Jackson is moving 121 cars. He can fit 11
cars on each lorry. How many lorries are
needed to move all of the cars at once?

Write the answers to the questions below.
See how quickly you can get them all right.

9 ÷ 3 =	3		90 ÷ 10 =	
8 ÷ 4 =			36 ÷ 4 =	
6 ÷ 1 =			48 ÷ 12 =	
12 ÷ 4 =			81 ÷ 9 =	
16 ÷ 8 =			49 ÷ 7 =	
20 ÷ 4 =			64 ÷ 8 =	
21 ÷ 7 =			45 ÷ 9 =	
18 ÷ 3 =			77 ÷ 11 =	
20 ÷ 2 =			60 ÷ 12 =	
30 ÷ 6 =			72 ÷ 6 =	
110 ÷ 10 =			108 ÷ 12 =	
48 ÷ 6 =			63 ÷ 9 =	

Fill in the blanks in the calculations below.

24 ÷ [4] = 6   [   ] ÷ 3 = 7

[   ] ÷ 7 = 6   144 ÷ [   ] = 12

80 ÷ [   ] = 8   [   ] ÷ 11 = 1

[   ] ÷ 8 = 11   48 ÷ [   ] = 6

More Number Facts

If you know one multiplication or division fact you can work out others. Here's an example:

From **6 × 5 = 30** you can work out that **5 × 6 = 30**

Division is opposite to multiplication, so you can also work out division facts.

30 ÷ 5 = 6
30 ÷ 6 = 5

Write two multiplication facts to match each division fact.

| 270 ÷ 3 = 90 |

| 3 × 90 = 270 |
| |

| 60 ÷ 15 = 4 |

| |
| |

Write two division facts to match each multiplication fact.

| 40 × 8 = 320 |

| 320 ÷ 40 = 8 |
| |

| 140 × 4 = 560 |

| |
| |

To multiply a number by a multiple of 10 or 100, you can use a simpler calculation to help.
Here's an example: **4 × 40 = ?**

Using your times tables, you know that **4 × 4 = 16**

40 is **10** times bigger than **4**, so the answer is **10** times bigger than **16**.

This means that **4 × 40 = 160**

Fill in the boxes to complete the calculations.

| 3 | × | 2 | = | 6 |
| 30 | × | 2 | = | 60 |

| 7 | × | 3 | = | |
| 7 | × | 30 | = | |

| 4 | × | 3 | = | |
| 4 | × | 30 | = | |

| 5 | × | 5 | = | |
| 500 | × | 5 | = | |

| 6 | × | 10 | = | |
| 60 | × | 10 | = | |

| 12 | × | 6 | = | |
| 12 | × | 600 | = | |

| 4 | × | 6 | = | |
| 4 | × | 60 | = | |

| 8 | × | 4 | = | |
| 8 | × | 400 | = | |

Complete the calculations and write the answers in the boxes.

20	×	8	=	160
50	×	8	=	
90	×	4	=	

7	×	60	=	
3	×	400	=	
6	×	300	=	

27

Problem Solving

Some maths questions won't tell you whether you need to multiply or divide. You'll need to decide what to do. Here's an example:

Jenna shares **42** fairy cakes between **7** people. **How many cakes will each person get?**

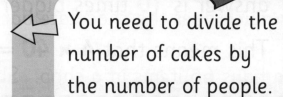

You need to divide the number of cakes by the number of people.

$42 \div 7 = 6$ so each person gets **6** cakes.

Answer the problems below. Write your answers in the boxes.

Farmer Dan has a trailer that moves 4 sheep at a time. How many journeys does he need to move 24 sheep?

Lena collects ice hockey cards. Each pack contains 9 cards. How many packs does she have to buy to get 45 cards?

Graham has 8 trays of 6 cabbage plants. How many plants does he have altogether?

Dev runs a restaurant. He has 5 tables that will each seat 12 customers. How many customers can he seat in his restaurant in total?

Steph orders 7 packs of 4 light bulbs. How many bulbs has she ordered altogether?

Work out the answers to these problems.

Grant has 3 types of fish in his pond. He has 8 of
each type. In total, how many fish does he have?

A bag of sweets costs 36p.
A chocolate bar costs half as much.
How much does the chocolate bar cost?

p

Anna buys 66 items in a shop. She wants to
split the shopping equally into 6 shopping bags.
How many items should she put in each bag?

There are 36 people travelling on a train with 3
carriages. Each carriage has the same number of
people. How many people are there in each carriage?

James buys a set of 7 books. It costs £21.
How much does each book cost?

£

There are 26 children in a class. Half of them
are girls. How many girls are there?

There are 72 people staying on a
campsite. Each tent holds 6 people.
How many tents are there in total?

Attila has 5 shirts and 4 ties. How many different
shirt and tie combinations can he wear?

It costs £4 to buy 2 ice creams.
How much does it cost to buy 6 ice creams?

£

Mixed Problems

Write the answers to these questions in the boxes.

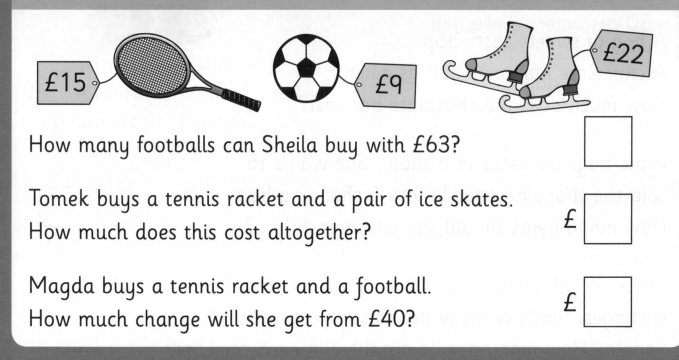

How many footballs can Sheila buy with £63?

Tomek buys a tennis racket and a pair of ice skates.
How much does this cost altogether?

£

Magda buys a tennis racket and a football.
How much change will she get from £40?

£

Solve these problems and write the answers in the boxes.

Keisha and 11 of her friends are going to a party
by taxi. If a taxi can carry 4 people, how many
will they need for everyone to get to the party?

Franklin wants to buy a chocolate bar for 65p. He
has 29p. How much more money does he need?

p

Notebooks cost £4 and pens cost £2.
How much does it cost to buy 3 of each?

£

Ravi pays £8 for each piano lesson.
Michael pays £55 in total for 5 piano lessons.
Who pays the most for each lesson?

Here are some more problems to work out in your head.
Write the answers in the boxes.

A shop has exactly
50 customers every day.
How many do they
have in 6 days?

One hen lays 6 eggs each
week. Another hen lays 4
eggs each week. How many
eggs will they lay in total
in 5 weeks?

One spaceship can hold 8
aliens. If there are 48 aliens,
how many spaceships are
needed to carry
them all?

Lottie buys 20 carrots,
40 potatoes and 25 tomatoes.
How many items has she
bought altogether?

Pardeep and his 3
friends each bake
12 cakes. How
many cakes do they
bake in total?

It takes Luke 30 minutes to
mow the lawn and 4 times
as long to wash the windows.
How many minutes does it
take him to wash
the windows?

A shop sells bracelets for £4
and necklaces for £3.
How much would two
sets of bracelets and
necklaces cost? £

All the Times Tables

One times table
1 × 1 = 1
2 × 1 = 2
3 × 1 = 3
4 × 1 = 4
5 × 1 = 5
6 × 1 = 6
7 × 1 = 7
8 × 1 = 8
9 × 1 = 9
10 × 1 = 10
11 × 1 = 11
12 × 1 = 12

Two times table
1 × 2 = 2
2 × 2 = 4
3 × 2 = 6
4 × 2 = 8
5 × 2 = 10
6 × 2 = 12
7 × 2 = 14
8 × 2 = 16
9 × 2 = 18
10 × 2 = 20
11 × 2 = 22
12 × 2 = 24

Three times table
1 × 3 = 3
2 × 3 = 6
3 × 3 = 9
4 × 3 = 12
5 × 3 = 15
6 × 3 = 18
7 × 3 = 21
8 × 3 = 24
9 × 3 = 27
10 × 3 = 30
11 × 3 = 33
12 × 3 = 36

Four times table
1 × 4 = 4
2 × 4 = 8
3 × 4 = 12
4 × 4 = 16
5 × 4 = 20
6 × 4 = 24
7 × 4 = 28
8 × 4 = 32
9 × 4 = 36
10 × 4 = 40
11 × 4 = 44
12 × 4 = 48

Five times table
1 × 5 = 5
2 × 5 = 10
3 × 5 = 15
4 × 5 = 20
5 × 5 = 25
6 × 5 = 30
7 × 5 = 35
8 × 5 = 40
9 × 5 = 45
10 × 5 = 50
11 × 5 = 55
12 × 5 = 60

Six times table
1 × 6 = 6
2 × 6 = 12
3 × 6 = 18
4 × 6 = 24
5 × 6 = 30
6 × 6 = 36
7 × 6 = 42
8 × 6 = 48
9 × 6 = 54
10 × 6 = 60
11 × 6 = 66
12 × 6 = 72

Seven times table
1 × 7 = 7
2 × 7 = 14
3 × 7 = 21
4 × 7 = 28
5 × 7 = 35
6 × 7 = 42
7 × 7 = 49
8 × 7 = 56
9 × 7 = 63
10 × 7 = 70
11 × 7 = 77
12 × 7 = 84

Eight times table
1 × 8 = 8
2 × 8 = 16
3 × 8 = 24
4 × 8 = 32
5 × 8 = 40
6 × 8 = 48
7 × 8 = 56
8 × 8 = 64
9 × 8 = 72
10 × 8 = 80
11 × 8 = 88
12 × 8 = 96

Nine times table
1 × 9 = 9
2 × 9 = 18
3 × 9 = 27
4 × 9 = 36
5 × 9 = 45
6 × 9 = 54
7 × 9 = 63
8 × 9 = 72
9 × 9 = 81
10 × 9 = 90
11 × 9 = 99
12 × 9 = 108

Ten times table
1 × 10 = 10
2 × 10 = 20
3 × 10 = 30
4 × 10 = 40
5 × 10 = 50
6 × 10 = 60
7 × 10 = 70
8 × 10 = 80
9 × 10 = 90
10 × 10 = 100
11 × 10 = 110
12 × 10 = 120

Eleven times table
1 × 11 = 11
2 × 11 = 22
3 × 11 = 33
4 × 11 = 44
5 × 11 = 55
6 × 11 = 66
7 × 11 = 77
8 × 11 = 88
9 × 11 = 99
10 × 11 = 110
11 × 11 = 121
12 × 11 = 132

Twelve times table
1 × 12 = 12
2 × 12 = 24
3 × 12 = 36
4 × 12 = 48
5 × 12 = 60
6 × 12 = 72
7 × 12 = 84
8 × 12 = 96
9 × 12 = 108
10 × 12 = 120
11 × 12 = 132
12 × 12 = 144